Endometriosis:

it's in not in your head, it's in your pelvis

Bethany Stahl

ISBN:
978-1-7323951-4-5 Paperback
978-1-7323951-5-2 Hardcover

Dedication

I want to take a moment and thank my compassionate and selfless husband, who has been with me through this entire process. He has supported and believed in my pain since the beginning.

Robert, I will never be able to thank you enough for helping me find my way, care for me during times of overwhelming pain and be the sole light in the dark when I was ready to give in. You are my earth angel, and I am forever grateful for the love you have given me.

Table of Contents

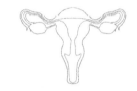

Introduction

I am not a doctor. My advice, suggestions, or treatments may not be for you, and that is okay. This book is designed to give you the tools, courage, and empowerment to seek out medical professionals who will provide the best treatment for your body.

I want to let you know that every endo journey is different when it comes to our pain, our experience, and our feelings. While you may relate and find comfort in knowing that you aren't the only one feeling this way, also know that if you have more or fewer symptoms than what I am experiencing, that doesn't mean you don't have endo or you aren't in the right place. Endo affects us all in different ways and that is part of the frustration with this disease.

You are not alone, and you have a whole group of endo warriors going through the same situation with you. I hope that hearing my story will make you laugh from understanding, cry over the sadness we go through, and smile because you know you aren't alone. The symptoms are not in your head. Remember that there are so many of us out there who are silently going through this crazy roller coaster of a chronic ilness together, and we are all right here with you.

My Endometriosis Journey

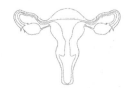

The Beginning

My heart raced with excitement as I got ready for dance class. I changed in the studio bathroom, pulling each leg through pink tights, pausing to use the restroom before wrapping myself into my leotard. It was then I noticed those little red spots in my flower print underwear. Fear set in as my heart felt like it was going to beat through my chest. Reeling, I knew from my fifth-grade health class that I was bleeding and those dots were what all those books and diagrams called a period.

I was eleven years old and utterly devastated. Having a period was embarrassing. I couldn't understand why so many of my friends bragged about getting theirs, treating it like a beautiful moment of womanhood. My first menstruation was fast and painless, but with each passing month, the more pain and suffering each period brought.

To help my understanding of puberty, my mom bought me a book about a girl who spoke to God about her periods. While the protagonist's biggest embarrassments were purchasing pads, mine were trying to walk down the hallway without blood gushing out my underwear, creatively tying jackets around my waist to mask any leakage. I made every attempt to appear as if I didn't feel like the school bully punched me in my stomach a hundred times over.

By the time I was thirteen, my periods were excruciating. They took me down to my knees, left me crying in a ball on the bathroom floor, cursing the universe that I was born with a vagina. I threw up the entire week of each period from the pain in my stomach; the pain felt like a man was pummeling his fists into me repeatedly, with knives clenched between his fingers.

My dad thought chocolate, heating pads, and magazines featuring my favorite boy bands could cure the pain, and while I was grateful and enjoyed the pampering, it didn't stop the excruciating suffering. The fierceness of my pain baffled me because my best friend could eat a tub of ice cream, take one ibuprofen, watch a sappy rom-com, and feel better. I envied her strength, but when we talked about cramps, she sounded like she was explaining the same thing I was enduring: horrific pain that tore our guts out one needle prick at a time. The cool kids in middle school must have been right. I was just a pathetic excuse for a human being.

Eventually, my mom took me to my first Ob-gyn appointment for help. Upon arriving at the office, a nurse quickly led us back to the exam room. She explained that I needed to change into a paper gown and told us that the doctor would be with us soon. I sat there shivering from the arctic cold of the office, terrified of what was to come. The door creaked open as the doctor walked into the room, along with a nurse. I was naked beneath a paper gown, as a grown man with a cumbersome mustache awkwardly made train noises while he probed a part of my body no one else has ever seen. The procedure made my stomach twist in fear, as I squeezed the life out of the nurse's hand and tried to suppress my tears. After a few more minutes, this quick exam by the family doctor showed that I was a normal healthy teenage girl. Great. So I was just pathetic.

The doctor suggested to my mother that I go on birth control (Depo-Provera) to try and regulate my periods, since they were never on time — always a week late or two weeks early. I didn't have a voice in the matter, just watched as two adults discussed the options of my reproductive health and made choices for a minor. My mom agreed, and so my fate was decided. Yo-ho, yo-ho, birth control for me.

Still shivering on the exam table, I listened to the conversation about my periods, my non-existent sex life, and the shot I was about receive. I thought about the girls I knew who were on birth control. They were cool because they were having sex. Boys liked them because they were open to everything. I wasn't even sure what everything was. None of my friends were on birth control yet, but then again, I wasn't taking the Depo so that I could have sex without worrying about getting pregnant; I was taking it to regulate my periods.

I pulled down the rim of my pants and the nurse injected the Depo shot. It would be effective for three months, and eventually my periods would stop, along with my pain. Simple and easy. One shot every three months, and I'd be fine. As we left the office, the doctor handed me a prescription for 500 mg. Naproxen tablets to eliminate any pain. Sweet, I had a cure.

That night, curled up beneath the covers of my bed, I thought again of how horrifying it was to have someone examine and even put their fingers inside of me without my consent. It brought back memories of the boy who sat behind me throughout seventh and eighth grade. I remembered how he used to stick his sweaty fingers into my underwear and drag his filthy hands across the seam of my pants, from knee to knee, at group tables. To me, the boy and the doctor were the same. Uninvited.

I swallowed hard in the dark, thinking back to the summer that boy found me on the playground. I had thought the middle school torture was over, but I was wrong. He shoved me onto the ground, and pinned me to the dirt. He was at least three times bigger than me, so it was futile to fight back. The attack felt like hours before I managed to wiggle a leg free and kick it between his legs, allowing myself a brief moment to escape. Now, I wondered if the experience could have been even worse if he had thought I was on birth control. Would he have been more aggressive? I had to keep the attack a secret, after all, when I told a trusted teacher what the boy had done during class, she told me that men would always be in charge of us — whether our boss, doctor, husband, or co-worker. We have to deal with it, she said. It is life.

She was wrong, and I should have continued to be brave and confide in someone else after she allowed the abuse to continue. In times like these, we must be warriors.

CHAPTER TWO

The High School Years

That August, as I walked through the doors of my high school for the first time, I felt freed from the repression of middle school. I was even allowed to wear flip-flops! Since only three or four other incoming students had attended middle school with me, I had the chance to start over. But soon I realized that high school, too, would be hard to endure because everyone tried to put me in a box. At the same time though, school was the only place I was able to be myself, so, ultimately, it became the personal hell that I loved to exist in.

During the first week of the new school year, a boy stole my heart the moment he clumsily walked into our freshman class wearing a football jersey of some team I had never heard of. We soon became best friends, and by sophomore year, we were going steady. I could genuinely say I was hopelessly in love. But this love wasn't all it was designed to be. Despite the year of Depo and pain pills my periods persisted. Over and over, I tried to explain to this boy I cared about that I wasn't lying about being on my period all of the time. My irregular cycles caused significant rifts between us because his friends

CHAPTER TWO

assured him that their girlfriends bled only three to five days each month. So, why was I bleeding at least seven to ten days—and that was during a light period. Often, when he wanted to go farther, I had to stop his wandering hands because I was on my period; my heart sank as I realized he thought I was being deceptive about my reason for stopping him.

During this time, I had a substantial period for six months straight. By this, I mean that I never stopped bleeding. Not even for an hour, not even for a minute. Before the six-month torture began, my periods had become highly irregular—from every other week to every two months, with no rhyme or reason.

At this point, I had been on birth control for nearly two years and, by now, I was begging for the Depo torture to end. During my periods, I took about four pills of the Naproxen a day, which just barely caused the pain to subside. To be honest, though, the Naproxen helped a little, and it was all I had to rely on since my last visit to the doctor. My pain had become worse than it ever had been before, keeping me in bed almost the entire week of my period. I was bleeding so much that putting in tampons up to ten times a day was making my insides raw.

I started talking to my friends about birth control to figure out how some of them were surviving flawlessly while taking it. So many of them were on the pill and had few or no side effects. Others didn't need the pill; they weren't having sex, and their periods weren't too heavy or painful. Compared to my friends, it seemed like I had been living a nightmare. I knew it was once again time to see that horrifying choo-choo train noisemaker, the Ob-gyn doctor.

Unfortunately, I was only fifteen and did not understand that doctors were not always right. I had no idea that there was value in gathering opinions. I thought every doctor must have the same knowledge base, and the idea of asking my parents to see a different doctor never crossed my mind. I sat on the table in the freezing office, as adults yet again decided my reproductive options for me. I was switched to non-continuous methods of birth control, which means taking all of the pills in a pack, including the placebos, to try and fix

10

the irregularity that was worsened by the Depo. But I was grateful for their decision when the doctor finally stopped making train noises while entering my body and prescribed me something I knew was working for my friends. His exam yet again revealed nothing more than that I was healthy, with bad periods, so I needed to keep taking pain-killers. He did mention that I had become anemic and would need iron pills to supplement my body during menstruation. Thanks Aunt Flo, you're awesome.

Trying to remember to take the pill every single day was just as much of a burden as trying to draw my eyeliner into a perfect line. But I began taking the birth control, and my periods did start to get better. They were no longer six months long, and my cycle returned to what I believed to be typical. Like those of all people who menstruate, or so I assumed, my period was coming either two weeks early or two weeks late and lasting for seven to ten days. My pain didn't decrease, but at this point, the doctor just told me that I had terrible periods and simply needed to be better with pain management. My brain heard more overdosing on the Naproxen, and less complaining—got it. I was weaker than my friends, and my pain tolerance must have been remarkably low.

I imagined my friends must have been superheroes when it came to pain. Yet, I remembered that I had once stepped on a broken bottle once and walked home, gushing blood for a good half-mile, before proceeding to pull out the glass, without wincing. And I knew that I had survived more falls than any girl in a teen movie—quite frequently falls down a flight of stairs—and that the pain never bothered me. I had always brushed it off. I was even able to dance through my gut-wrenching cramps for more than ten hours of practice, vomiting only once or twice, and still nailed every move. But yet, the other girls never puked. They never faltered. They never sat hunched in class, cradling their stomachs. I felt defeated when I saw tampon commercials that featured girls playing sports while on their periods. That depiction of periods felt so unrealistic: like, yes—let me kick this ball and twist with a smile; when, in reality, I would likely vomit all over everyone else and crawl to the goal in a modified fetal position, thanking the sun for becoming a natural heating pad along the way.

In our conversations, my friends said they also hated cramps. I figured this must mean they were puking their guts up every month, too, but just not at school. They, too, must have been regularly feeling the punch in the stomach alongside the knife-twirling pain that prevented me from even speaking coherently. I couldn't understand how one or two Ibuprofens a month would help them. It baffled me, yet they were so convincing in their reassurance that a few pills was all it took. Again and again, I thought I just had a low pain tolerance; after all, what else could have been wrong? I had seen the doctor; he had checked me over time and time again; and nothing was ever wrong. Ever.

My psyche started to attack itself. My peers bullied me in school, so I was weak. Teachers bullied me with rumors that were being spread about me, so I was pathetic. I believed I had allowed someone to sexually harass me for more than two years, and that made me stupid. My periods took the life out of me because I was lazy. I began to self-harm and was clinically diagnosed with "teen depression" in high school. At that point, I felt as if depression was only one more flaw to peg to the board of being a worthless human.

A year had passed since I started taking the pill, and I was sixteen. Even my own family had forgotten the original reason why I was on birth control: to prevent pain and regulate periods. It had become routine for a family member and I to have talks in the bathroom about why I had missed my period; these conversations included nonstop questions about who I was sleeping with, and threat of a pregnancy test if I didn't start bleeding soon. My soul shattered as I had to defend myself, insisting that I had never had sex and endlessly explaining that I honestly did have irregular periods that I couldn't control. Family and friends shamed me for being on a medication that had been prescribed to me.

Later in my high school years, I started becoming sexually active. Sexual activity was a confusing experience. There were times when I was fingered, and I felt my body melting with pleasure, just like everyone said. But there were other times when I lay in bed, curled in a ball for hours afterward, feeling as if sharp sticks had been inside of me instead. When I mentioned the strange pain to my friends, they told me to tell my partners to trim their fingernails. I was merely feeling a little pinch, they assured me. My friends also told me that I was just new to all of this—it would take time to get comfortable and loosen up. No biggie. It was normal.

I stopped talking to my family about the pain because I knew they would reject me if I talked about sex. I didn't want to add another negative aspect to their suspicions about my already irregular periods and their threats of pregnancy tests. Sex before marriage was taboo, according to my family, and they openly hated the boy I was in love with, forbidding me to see him. My entire life had become a web of secrecy, confusion, and lies. I relied on the internet and strangers in chatrooms to help me understand some of the painful experiences I was having when I felt too embarrassed to confide in my friends. Even then, the strangers assured me I was fine.

I accepted the strange pains and gave my boyfriend the nail-trimming advice, but every tenth time or so, the experience felt just awful. I had watched the mainstream movies about sexual activities hurting for the first few times and assumed my pain must have been normal, just as everyone always said. But vaginal sex still terrified me, and I couldn't admit the truth of why. If pain really was what I could expect time and time again, then I never wanted to have sex. Where was the pleasure in it?

Soon, the time finally came. I was a junior in high school, and that day I was feeling like I was on top of the world. I was still with my long-term boyfriend—the same boy I had met at the start of my freshman year—and I was madly in love with him. We had spent a fantastic day together, a day that was unlike any other time in our relationship. After swimming and hanging out by the pool, we retreated to his bedroom. I knew the time was approaching. My heart pounded, as I felt his hands slip off my bikini. He was in front of me, moving so slowly, being caring and careful. But a moment later, I was screaming on the inside, and I can only imagine the horror re-

13

flected in my face as he was trying to go inside of my body.

I felt the pain shoot up my uterus, through my core, and into my breasts. It felt like lightning as it went down through my thighs. I bit my lip and told myself to do it. The pain was supposed to be there, everyone felt like this. I loved him. Sex was supposed to hurt, and I was supposed to be in excruciating pain. Connecting with him would be completely worth it; that's what everyone said. But I couldn't. Wetness, positions, the fact that we had done a ton of sexual activity even before that day—none of it mattered. The pain was like a knife trying to filet my flesh open from the inside out. And the fear of letting him down was even worse. I looked into his dark eyes and asked him if he would always love me, no matter what. He just stared back at me, silent, still trying to work himself into me. That was the moment I knew I wasn't going to suffer through the discomfort for him. Sex wasn't worth the excruciating pain. I couldn't go through with it. A few days later, I found myself without a boyfriend.

I felt physically broken. I had lost what I thought was love and began to hate my body for being so useless. For the previous two or three months, my period had finally become regular, arriving at the same time each month. After the experience with my boyfriend, though, I happened to miss my next period, and I was overcome by the worst realization. I could be pregnant. After all, a quick internet search informed me that if a man ejaculates pre-sex, and if the pre-ejaculate goes inside of the woman, it is rare but possible to get pregnant. Oh, holy hell.

I was sixteen and terrified. My brother had been just a bit older than I was now when he found out he would be having a child. I saw the struggle he went through, and I knew even then that there was no way I could handle the situation as well as he did. Each day, I debated talking to my ex about my late period. On one hand, I knew it was stupid to think that I was pregnant—that it was simply not possible. On the other hand, shouldn't I take a pregnancy test before we passed the no-turning-back zone? My family members had already proven to be fertile, so there was definitely a possibility. Would we try to make it work if I was pregnant? No. I couldn't even think like that. I wasn't pregnant. I wasn't going to be a teen mom. I couldn't be.

Another month late. Do I tell him now? What do I even say? Would I be considered a crazy ex for telling him my suspicions or a crazy ex for not telling him and really being pregnant? I know that what happened wasn't really sex like movie sex, but crazier things have happened. Yeah, I get weird periods, and I know I'm on birth control — but I forget to take the pills all the time. Did those white pills count as missed days, too? I always forget to take those. Finally, after I was a few days late for what would be the third month without a period, I approached him in the hallway. With my heart pounding out of my chest and shaking my vision, I slipped a note into his hand, asking him to meet me in the staircase, where we could be alone. When I saw him come down the staircase, he didn't stop, but it was my only chance to set the record straight. Crazy or not, I had to tell him. If there was even a slight possibility that a pregnancy would mean holding a leash to eighteen years of his life, he deserved to know.

"So . . . I know we don't talk anymore, and you're dating someone new, but . . . I could maybe possibly be potentially . . . pregnant," I looked up at him, praying for any understanding, for the best friend who used to be behind those eyes to tell me I wasn't pregnant and that everything would be okay.

"We didn't even have sex, so I don't know what crazy shit you are even talking about," he spoke coldly, rolling his eyes, leaving me standing in the staircase alone.

A few weeks later, my period finally came. It would be an especially painful one, since the more time that elapsed between each cycle, the worse the pain felt. I began to feel like I deserved all the pain. With each gut-wrenching twist, I let myself feel the agony. I stopped taking medicine to try and suppress the cramping. The Naproxen pills were no longer useful for preventing pain, anyway. This period produced the most pain I had experienced in my life, thus far, and I was ready to die rather than deal with it any longer. After two weeks of misery, the torture finally stopped. After that, my periods started to return to what I assumed to be normal in terms of regularity and pain level.

At school, rumors spread about me not putting out for my ex. Random girls approached me, telling me that I was pathetic because I "was incapable of handling a penis" or that my ex just needed a "real woman to handle him." My heart ached as I realized that these random people knew intimate details of that day; their perspective was one-sided, though, missing any details that may have incriminated my ex. The non-stop harassment made me question my sexuality. Perhaps the whispers in the hallways about me being a lesbian were true. Girls were nice, but I wasn't sure I was sexually attracted to them. Was it just the way I was raised that was convincing me I was straight? Maybe the pain was just my mind telling me that I wasn't into boys. That I wasn't into my ex. It was confusing, and once again, I allowed the world to control how I felt about my own body.

During this distressing time, I started to feel overcome by dizziness as I walked between classes. The walls and floors around me would spin, become fuzzy and dark, and I could feel my legs collapsing beneath me. The dizziness happened over and over again, and my mom assured me that she had felt the same way in high school. It was just my blood-sugar. Just eat a spoonful of peanut butter, and I'd be good to go. A jar later, though, and I still felt the same. Faint, dizzy, and now nauseous from the amount of food I had ingested.

My parents took me to a cardiologist who required that I wear an embarrassing heart monitor to school for a week, where, of course, it was bumped and started playing back discordant noises. The entire class laughed at me. The whispers, pointing, and laughter from classmates was overwhelming. I could hear the chatter: Look! It was the girl who was unable to keep a guy pleased and who had become physically broken after their break up. Ha!

The cardiologist saw nothing significant from the results of the monitor and wrote off the dizziness as broken-heart syndrome. I just needed to get over the breakup. His diagnosis didn't make sense, though, because I thought I was over my past relationship. It had now been several months since my ex left. My heart had moved on, as I fell more deeply in love with a friend, turned best friend, and now boyfriend. When the dizziness persisted, I knew it was just another part of life I'd need to learn to live with.

As my junior year of high school came to an end, I started experiencing mid-to-lower back pain so severe that some days I couldn't walk or move. It was so excruciating that I gave up dancing, an art I had loved since I was three. My discomfort was most intense when the back pain coupled with my period. During these times, the pain utterly crippled me, and I even had to miss a few days of school. My parents took me to a primary care doctor who noticed that I had acute scoliosis and referred me to a physical therapist. I practiced a series of exercises to strengthen my core muscles in an attempt to diminish the feeling of being whipped to death across my lower back. The physical therapists were baffled because the amount of pain I was experiencing did not align with the condition they believed was causing it. Despite the physical therapy, the only remedy that significantly helped ease the pain was the massages my boyfriend gave me. Eventually, I quit going to physical therapy because the therapist suggested, after months of no improvement, that I continue with the massages from my boyfriend and I'd be fine. Good work, P.T.

During the summer before my senior year of high school, I was able to enroll in college courses; this meant that I would need to attend high school only in the mornings, for an hour or so. I started my first college course the day before my seventeenth birthday. Luckily, my boyfriend was extremely talented at pushing on all the right places in my back to relieve the pain, making my quality of life so much better during my senior year. While my parents hated the idea of him sitting on top of me in bed, rubbing lotion into my back, I was completely enamored by his ability to be my best friend as well as the only person who had ever helped relieve the pain. He was a blessing I hoped I would always have in my life.

I began taking frequent baths to let the heat radiate through the core of my body. The water's even heat helped alleviate the cramping so much more efficiently than a heating pad. Spending hours locked away in the bathroom, soaking in the hot water, improved not only the nausea caused by extreme pain, but also my happiness.

CHAPTER TWO

Since I was in enrolled in college for senior year, my schedule was flexible enough to allow me to frequently lie down between classes. I didn't realize that the unconventional schedule was doing wonders for taking pressure off of my body and alleviating my symptoms. I was happy and content: I was in love with a funny, caring boy, almost done with high school drama, and finally living my life.

As my senior year came to an end, I made every attempt to let the pain that had consumed my life die on graduation day. No more bullies; no more run-ins with my ex; no more accusations of being slutty and not putting out at the same time; no more weekly interrogations about whether I was pregnant. I was done with the drama. Two weeks after graduating from high school, I moved out of the only home I had known and left the city I was living in. I swore I would never go back. This city held my body hostage, wrapped in baggage and pain, but now I was going to be free. I was moving into a university to take on my next adventure. New mindset. New life. New me.

CHAPTER THREE

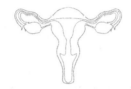

Early Adulthood

*L*iving on my own in a college dorm that summer was both exciting and terrifying. The best part was, my boyfriend started college early to be able to spend the summer with me, and he lived only two floors above me. We spent every day together—studying, roaming the campus, and, most excitingly, having sex. One weekend, his room-mate left for a holiday break, and we had the weekend to ourselves. We had spent all day in his room, trying to watch this new streaming service everyone was raving about while being distracted by each other's tender kisses. Before either of us knew it, we were having the most breathtaking, toe-curling sex, breaking every negative stigma surrounding what I thought intimacy would be like.

It felt inexplicably freeing, like an out of body experience. The moment lasted forever as the feeling only became more intoxicating until we climaxed together. We cuddled in each other's arms and laughed, pleasantly surprised at how we both enjoyed it. Giggling, we went downstairs to dinner, our feet bouncing off the floor as if we were just balloons of helium. Sex was startlingly fun, and the feeling was something I couldn't shake from my mind.

As the end of summer approached, I asked my boyfriend to move into an apartment with me. I was newly eighteen, which meant I could rent, and he would be turning eighteen in a matter of months. Though apprehensive, we both agreed that living together was smarter financially (well at least that's the reasoning we explained to our parents) and decided to leap into the next stage of our relationship.

By the end of my first year at college, I was nineteen. My life had been progressing more quickly than I could even process. I was renting an impressive apartment with a community hot tub in this college town. I was officially living with a supportive boyfriend who had been with me now for a few years; attending a state university to gain my bachelor's degree; working my first job; and paying for my education and half of our bills all on my own. Did I mention the apartment complex had a hot tub? Oh, I did. There was nothing better than melting my pain away every evening in the piping hot water.

Baths and hot-tub time became a staple in my life to help the pain melt away. After a particularly horrible shift at work—a theme park where I was on my feet all day and soaked from the rain, I opened the door to a rose-petal path leading to a candlelit bubble bath. My boyfriend knew that no matter what, I felt a million times better after having the heat melt through my muscles and relax my body. We were still having sex, but occasionally, the way his penis hit the walls inside of me caused a burst of pain, making me vomit. I was embarrassed because I wasn't sure why sex would affect me so harshly sometimes, yet at other times it was beyond cathartic.

At this point, I hadn't seen the Ob-gyn since I was about sixteen. I didn't want to. The doctor was awkward, and those distressing train noises he made before he probed my body with his instruments or fingers made me feel so violated. I couldn't stand to put myself through that again. In addition, during the past few years, I had learned that everything I had told the doctor in confidence had been relayed directly back to my family, even though they didn't have the right to know all about my reproductive health and sexual life. I felt a lack of safety when in the Ob-gyn office, and I was skeptical about the need for yet another exam that always revealed nothing was wrong.

Despite my reluctance and against my better judgment, I made an appointment with the Ob-gyn doctor and told him that I had still been experiencing heavy and painful periods. I didn't mention the occasional pain I felt during sex because it didn't happen often, and, by now, I honestly felt that discomfort was just a part of sex, for all women. Intercourse felt good, amazingly pleasing most times, but there were moments when it was just a little more uncomfortable than others. A little poke here, a sharp pain there, nothing abnormal. I didn't talk to friends about sex either — all we ever spoke about were complex organic chemistry reactions, as we worked towards our degrees. Besides, most of these girls weren't dating at this stage of college; I wouldn't have been, either, had I not found the one. However, it just furthered my thoughts that there was nothing noteworthy to mention to the Ob-gyn.

The doctor told me to continue taking the birth control he had prescribed because it would keep regulating my periods. He explained that perceived pain is measured on a scale, and that the experience of pain is all relative. What may be a lot of pain for me may not objectively be a lot of pain. Then, making me doubt myself even more, a nurse in the office mentioned that heavy periods were associated more with heavy women, and since I was barely over a hundred pounds, my periods weren't all that bad, after all. I left the office feeling defeated, and reached into my pocket to grab my phone and call my boyfriend, telling him about the conclusion of the Ob-gyn visit. Once again, I felt hopeless — on the inside, still the miserable girl from middle school.

I relinquished the belief that there was a gynecological cause for my struggles. Every time I had gone to the Ob-gyn doctor, I had gotten nowhere. Still, though, I felt like my body was slowly degrading. A year of college had passed, and the dizziness I had felt in high school had continue to worsen.

One day, after dressing in my water repellant shirt and shorts for my shift at the theme park, I started my drive to work. As I drove, I began to feel the world sway around me. I knew I had missed too much work already, and I couldn't afford to call off. I blinked hard and took a deep breath. I could do this. I had to do this. Ten hours. No big deal.

I persevered and made it through the first several hours of my shift. When it was finally time for my break, I walked into the air-conditioned break room, and grabbed a sports drink, pausing to go to the bathroom to vomit and then ate a quick protein-packed meal to replace the contents I just rid from my body. The world was still spinning as I put my feet up on a chair, counting down the thirty minutes of my break. Five minutes were left, and I still had to walk back to my location, but, first, my stomach was about to explode. I ran to the bathroom, where I continued to vomit while simultaneously enduring a bout of diarrhea. Two minutes. I'd have to run in order to get back to the office before I was written up. I took an anti-diarrheal pill and put on a panty shield to be safe. This kind of nausea wasn't uncommon before an unexpected period. This was normal.

Standing back at my post in the African themed park, I noticed the people walking by becoming wavy, and I felt my cheeks, as well as the tip of my nose, start to tingle and become numb despite the ninety-degree weather. I knew I had minutes before I was going to collapse. This job was remarkably frustrating in terms of the restrictions placed on the employees. If an emergency — such as my imminent collapse — happened, there was a nearby phone we were allowed to use; however, the phone was located behind a door we weren't allowed to access without a second team member. The emergency phone rule usually wouldn't have been a big problem, yet because we were understaffed, I was working at my location alone. The reasoning behind the rule was that there was a brief moment when the employee would not be monitored by company cameras. In that short moment, I could have had the opportunity to steal cash out of the apron I wore around my waist (we didn't have registers). By even taking the risk to go off-camera, I could be fired. The edges of my vision darkened as I contemplated the rules. If I was going to call for help, I had to go to the phone without a co-worker. Damn. Collapse, and be pillaged by sweaty theme-park visitors for the hundreds of dollars around my waist or risk losing my job and get medical attention? If I could guarantee someone was actively watching the cameras, I would have opted to collapse because I needed this job. I couldn't jeopardize the whopping minimum wage I was making. Ultimately I decided to risk it, and call for a supervisor who didn't hate me; he ran from the office over to my location catching me just as I collapsed, and took me to the nurse's office.

After I spent a few hours in the nurse's office, hydrating with more sports drinks, a few of the other supervisors wanted me to return to work. I knew I couldn't, though—I needed to go home. When I arrived at my apartment complex, I could barely ascend the stairs to my second-floor apartment. Meanwhile, my boyfriend was still at work in another department at the theme park. I was unable to contact him due to the insane phone rules in place. So, I called family who lived in a nearby town who insisted they take me to a local hospital because I knew something was terribly wrong.

I was admitted to the hospital, where I stayed for two full days. During that time, doctors ordered an MRI and blood work, both of which came back normal. They then repeatedly tested me for vertigo. Again, everything was normal. At this point, the family members who drove me to the hospital mentioned to the doctor that they had an allergy to blue food dye, which caused them to feel similar light-headed symptoms. They insisted that I could be experiencing a similar allergic reaction because my birth control pills were blue. Unbelievably, I was diagnosed with an allergy to blue food dye based on my family's suggestion but no scientific evidence. I was released from the hospital without further testing or examination.

I had been written up at my job for missing multiple shifts, even though I had called off from the hospital bed. Eventually, the supervisors forced me to quit by making me work multiple thirteen-hour shifts, back to back, with less than five hours between the end of one shift and start of another. When I left the theme park job, I knew this would be the start of a slippery slope, with employers not taking my illnesses seriously, and the thought terrified me.

Luckily I was fortunate enough to find a new job quickly. I secured a job at the university I was attending, as well as a private-practice animal clinic. Working two positions was necessary. I was stealing toilet paper from public restrooms to save money for food and medical bills, pushing myself through cramping, now even sometimes not on my period, past my breaking point, to make ends meet, and trying to focus on my education—all while trying to maintain my relationship with my boyfriend and not allowing the stress of life to separate us. About six months had passed since the incident at the theme park before I was in the hospital again after becoming overwhelmingly dizzy and injuring my foot falling down a flight of stairs. The diagnosis that the wet floors caused by a rainy day plus an overworked college student was the perfect equation for a clumsy sprain. Was I overworked? Absolutely. However, being overworked wasn't unusual among my peers who were also struggling to afford schooling and housing on low-paying jobs. I was stressed, sure, but not to the point that I would collapse down a staircase.

Aside from the stress, I began experiencing mood swings from new birth control pills (that were no longer blue) which become increasingly intense. At times they were so extreme that I felt insane. I would go from crying to laughing to raging in anger and then crying from laughing. During these times, hormones overtook my body, and I could feel my real-self trapped on the inside, screaming to get out. I said things I didn't mean, and I was hurt by words that shouldn't have made me cry. I knew it was time to let my own body take care of itself and get off of all medicine. Something had to change, so I stopped taking birth control. Why was I even still on the pill? The only reason I had even started taking birth control was because a doctor told me to do so when I was a child. He claimed the drug would help me, but it never did. At this point, I didn't have to comply with a suggestion to take medication. So, I was done; there was no way I was going to cause my own insanity.

After a few months without birth control pills, I felt like a new person. My mood improved dramatically, and I felt like I had been restored to the person I used to be. I was happy and in control of my life again, despite the chaos that came with being a struggling college student. My periods were still painful and irregular, but in the same way they had always been, so, I assumed, thankfully, that I was back to normal. The one thing that didn't change was the dizziness that had become so severe it was affecting me daily. I had even stopped driving because of how irregular the symptoms would occur.

I was still on the hunt to figure out why I was having mysterious fainting episodes. However, I no longer had health insurance. I had to choose between paying for insurance and paying rent. When I stopped paying for insurance, I tried to save as much money as I could for visits with specialists. I visited general practitioners, cardiologists, endocrinologists, and neurologists—and none of them could find anything wrong with me. The answers were always "overworked," "dehydrated," "worn-thin," all simple explanations for something that had been so wrong for what felt like my entire life. I was frustrated because the diagnosis always matched what was occurring in my life at the moment. As a young teen, I was just being dramatic about period pain. In high school, the cause was a broken heart; in college, it was stress. In reality, though, I had been experiencing these same symptoms forever, so how could they be caused by something new in my life?

An entire year had passed since I stopped taking birth control pills, and despite the symptoms I was still experiencing, it was my best year in a long time. My body continued to have more regulated periods and even less pain. The dizziness also started to improve. I realized that my body preferred to be free of any birth control medications, and I swore that I would never go back on the pill again. I wanted to live as drug-free as possible, since I knew I was so easily affected. My life seemed perfect for a bit. Yes, I still had painful periods, which I thought everyone experienced. But the pain was nothing compared to how excruciating it had felt when I was on birth control. I was undoubtedly happy and ended my search for answers.

Adulthood

I was almost finished with my undergraduate degree, thank god. I was now twenty-one and married to my boyfriend of four and a half years. I was blissfully happy. Like many women, I had experienced a handful of pregnancy scares that started to wear on me. There were a few times that other birth control methods weren't used, but despite my late periods, every pregnancy test was negative. Always. The singular line on the pregnancy test became disheartening because while, yes, we weren't planning on having children, my heart hoped to one day experience the excitement of seeing those two little lines on a pregnancy test. After all, I was a product of the culture I grew up in: grade school, high school, college, marriage, babies.

A heated night between my husband and me ended with us having unprotected sex; after the lust faded and realization set in, we panicked. Would I get pregnant? No, not us. How many times had we been through this? A few weeks passed, and my period still hadn't come. It would likely come in a day or so—but my breasts were abnormally sore, I was experiencing unusual nausea, and, overall, I just felt pregnant. I refused to take a test but eventually gave in to myself. It showed the same result as always. Negative.

I was now a month late, and my period still hadn't come. A sense of dread settled in when I realized that I still had no health insurance and new Ob-gyn offices wouldn't accept me as a self-paying new patient. I had only one option. I made an appointment with the appalling mustached doctor, Mr. Ob-gyn, but this time, I'd have my husband with me for support. My flat stomach had sprouted the smallest little bump, as the symptoms progressed. In the doctor's office, I had a blood test and a urine test, neither of which confirmed I was absolutely pregnant. At this point, I would been five to six weeks pregnant, with increasing hCG levels that should have been able to yield a one-hundred percent positive test.

I made a follow-up appointment a week later for an internal sonogram. By now, my tummy had a little bump, and my weight had increased a more few pounds. My husband and I waited anxiously, staring at the fuzzy screen, until the nurse panned over a little bubble. I had recently been working in an animal shelter, performing sonograms on pregnant dogs, and I knew what we had just seen: a gestational sac. The nurse turned away the screen from my sightline, so I couldn't see the embryo. I knew it would still be small at six to seven weeks with unidentifable features. I searched the expression on the nurse's face for any sign of acknowledgment that I was pregnant, knowing at this point that I'd either be having a baby or a miscarriage.

"Congratulations! How long has it been since the positive test?" The nurse smiled at us as we sat there in shock. I darted a glance at my husband, and tears filled of happiness came to both our eyes. There was an embryo and we were pregnant!

"We haven't had the positive yet," I said, worried that something was already wrong.

She gasped, her eyes flashing back to the screen as she pulled the sonogram probe aggressively out of my body, nearly dropping it, and ran out of the room. My heart was pounding so loudly that I was sure the entire office could hear it echoing like a broken drum.

"What's happening?" I asked my husband, feeling tears on my face. This time, though, they were tears of fear. I knew something was wrong. I hadn't been able to see the screen clearly enough to tell if there was the little white blip of an embryo or if it looked okay. I asked my husband to describe what he saw; but he confirmed that he did see the gestational sac and that he, too, was unsure of whether or not he had seen an embryo, having no idea what he was looking at.

Sitting in silence, my husband and I knew something had to be wrong. More than thirty minutes later, the nurse returned and walked us out of the office, telling me to call back and make a follow-up appointment to go over the sonogram results with the doctor. She refused to answer the question of whether or not I was expecting, so I made the appointment. The doctor wouldn't be able to see me for another month.

My stomach grew for just a couple more weeks, then stopped. The few pounds I gained stayed, but the little bump started to disappear. The symptoms had waned, and in my heart, I didn't feel pregnant any more. My husband had already taken off from work for my two previous appointments, and his request for time off to go to the follow-up visit was denied. I should have been ten or eleven weeks at this point, but I wasn't confident that embryo was viable, or even alive.

My name was called out in the room full of women with big bellies, and I stood alone, walking over to the nurse, who escorted me into the doctor's office. I sat in the room, waiting. The wall clock ticked so loudly that I could count every single second that passed. When the doctor came in, he sat across from me and asked, with a blank expression, why I had made the appointment to meet with him.

"We are supposed to go over my sonogram results. I might be pregnant." My voice shook with fear.

"It was normal. Just a late period. Take this." He spoke tersely, reaching into the drawer of his desk and taking white pill out of a silver packet.

"Normal? The nurse saw something," I retorted.

"Nope. Just take this, and you will have your period in just a day or so." He placed the pill in my hand, along with a cup of water. In utter shock, I stupidly took the pill, not thinking to ask what it was before he started to walk out of the office.

"Can I see the photos from the sonogram?" I asked, as he made his way out of the doorway.

"There were no photos," his voice echoed.

I walked out of the office, got into my car, and sat there crying. The doctor had said nothing about the sonogram, said there was never an embryo. He refused to show me the images, refused to discuss it further, simply handed me the pill and told me to take it. I was overwhelmed by his denial that I was pregnant, or that I had miscarried (which is what I was expecting). Instead, I was given a white tablet, with no explanation of what it was, and then pushed out of the office without any further care. I left feeling beaten down and saddened by the reality that I wasn't pregnant.

By the next day, the mysterious pill was making me feel as if every single organ was being ripped out through my vagina and then stuffed back in. I missed college classes for a week and was physically unable to get off of the couch or stay conscious for more than a few hours at a time. I bled orange blood, as vibrant as a sports drink, and endured the worst pain as I passed thick clumps of uterine lining. It was unlike anything I had ever seen or experienced.

I had eventually gotten the courage to call the office and question them. After a battle of the receptionist refusing to release my medical records, I finally gained limited access. The results of the sonogram were "inclusive without images". There was no record of the doctor giving me any medication. With further investigation, I learned that orange blood is caused by bleeding along with cervical fluid, which is known to happen after a miscarriage.

After that experience, I swore that I would never again see another Ob-gyn. This feeling solidified when the bill for the ultrasound was mailed to my childhood home instead of my current address on record. I received a call from a family member had who opened the mail, pressing me about the reason for my ultrasound. They repeatedly questioned me about a pregnancy until I gave in, crying, and revealed something I had wanted to keep just between my husband and me.

Nothing was the same after this. Shortly after the experience, I began having frequent, severe pain with sex. There were so many moments when sex felt as if my husband's penis was a serrated knife. Not every time was this painful, but the more time that passed, the more excruciating intimacy became. My periods again became extremely irregular, ranging from a few days to two months between each cycle.

CHAPTER FIVE

Crumbling

Working for an animal shelter, I was pursuing my childhood dream of becoming a veterinarian while finishing up my degree. On this particular morning, I drove to work hunched behind the wheel, shaking my leg in pain, hoping the handful of pain meds I took would start to kick in. I was hurting so badly that I knew I wouldn't make it through the day, but we needed the money and the animals needed me. I had to get through my shift, for them. Once I arrived at the shelter, I lasted only about ten minutes before throwing up in the restroom. I sat on the floor in the small converted closet, and was covered in cold sweat, hating myself for feeling this sick. I forced myself to stand and splashed my face with water. Making eye contact with myself in the filthy mirror, and I knew I was unable to stay any longer.

In the adjacent room, I overheard one of my coworkers tell the rest of the staff that she was having a little cramping and was going home to binge-watch a new show. I walked out of the bathroom and saw her run around the counter in the middle of the room, sipping a coffee topped with whip cream, and joking with the rest of our coworkers. She was laughing loudly and smiling, in keeping with her usual outgoing personality, and she showed no signs of being in pain. At that moment, I was reminded that my cramps weren't normal.

I knew that my coworker was likely not lying — that she actually was cramping — and that made the situation even more frustrating for me, in that I wished I felt good enough to move like she was, despite cramping. I would have gladly stayed. Unfortunately, only one person was allowed to go home that day, if it was necessary, because we were understaffed. I knew this, yet I forced myself to talk to the supervisor and confess that I been throwing up and wanted — no I needed — to go home, too. But since my coworker had seniority and had a higher ranked position in our department, she got the go-ahead, and I had to stay.

I survived two more painful hours before I fainted from the pain and was taken to the hospital. In the ER, the hospital staff ran no tests, besides taking my blood pressure and gave me a saline drip. My diagnosis was stress from being in my last semester of college and from being overworked. The ER nurse suggested an additional piece of the diagnosis since nothing was found medically: "Who didn't want a day off of work?" Last time I checked, there wasn't a sign-up sheet for losing pay, passing out in front of coworkers, and owing more than three-thousand dollars for a saline drip and a pat on the head. Again, I swore off doctors, vowing that I'd never return to the ER, because of my frustration with these doctors who had been ignoring me.

I was livid. I had seen every specialist. I had been to the hospital multiple times, admitted for days sometimes, and I had been cleared over and over again by the Ob-gyn. I still had no idea what was causing my symptoms, but I had come to a conclusion. I must be a sick, weak excuse for a human. I was likely just unhealthy and would die young. Over the years I started to notice a correlation between colds and period symptoms. It felt as if my immune system was weak, and I was sick all the time, especially the weeks surrounding my period.

A cold was sure to always come to suck away my energy before I was zapped with pain.

Eventually, I quit working. I wasn't able to lift animals in surgery without unbearable pain. Standing hurt, crouching hurt, existing hurt, and life was miserable. I was about to graduate with my degree in biology and continue on to veterinary school. I wouldn't be without a job for long; surely, a desk job would open up somewhere. Besides, I was applying to veterinary schools — I would be relocating soon anyway.

During this time of transition, I thought a lot about the loss of the pregnancy; although I knew that having a baby while I was working on my doctorate would be foolish, I couldn't stop thinking about the idea of a family. As the deadline for veterinary school applications neared, reality set in. I started to realize that I may not be physically able to complete veterinary school. If I was unable to do my job at the animal shelter, it seemed clear that I wouldn't be able to become a veterinarian. Ultimately, I came to the conclusion that if I had to choose between graduate school toward a career I may not be able to handle physically and the hope of a family, I wanted to choose the latter. I withdrew my application to veterinary programs and hoped the universe had a plan for me.

A week later, I was in the tub trying to soak out the ongoing pain, when the screen of my phone lit up. Looking at the caller ID, I saw that it was the veterinary school application service calling me. I answered, apprehensive about the reason for their call.

"Hello?" I asked, unsure of the response.

"Is this Bethany?" a woman asked.

"Yes . . ." I replied cautiously.

"We saw that you didn't submit your application for veterinary school, and despite the deadline that passed, we wanted to offer you the opportunity to apply late. We understand that you are a prime candidate, and we can blame technology for your tardy application. Laptop failure? Just tell me the schools you want, and we will make sure they consider you. We can give you three days to finish and submit your application."

CHAPTER FIVE

My heart pounded. This was a call that didn't happen for everyone. The deadline was the deadline. I had worked so hard for this. I built a pre-veterinary program at my college, volunteered over one thousand hours, and worked in multiple veterinary centers—all toward this moment. I had paid for this opportunity with four years of hardship, sometimes living in poverty, to be here. I had become the president of the American Pre-Veterinary Medical Association and was recognized by Dr. Jane Goodall for building conservation programs in schools, all for this moment. And now, without submitting my application, I was being given a hand to extend the deadline.

"Thank you. But I'm not applying," I said, knowing I couldn't do it.

"Are you sure? This is your last chance," she was clearly shocked at my decision.

"I'm sure," I replied, hanging up the phone and sobbing into the tub.

In the eyes of my family and friends, there was no reason for my decision to abandon my childhood dream. My family was devastated when I told them I was choosing not to attend veterinary school. That I wouldn't be a doctor. They didn't speak to me for a month after I shared the news with them. When I told supportive college faculty members about my decision, their mouths dropped. Even the faculty who attended my wedding didn't speak to me. I knew I was now a disappointment, when I had showed so much promise. How could I possibly explain that I chose to abandon my career because of an invisible illness I believed had?

Abruptly, I was faced with choosing another career path. Within a literal day, I started an art career. I had painted a few times throughout college, and I wasn't half bad at it. Art attracted me, largely because, I was able to create while lying in bed during extended periods of extreme pain. I started working as hard as I could to create a job that would accommodate me when I needed more than a week off every month. If I were my own boss, no one could be angry or tell me no.

Meanwhile, with only one of us making an income, we were

struggling financially. Despite kicking off selling my paintings, I was relentlessly applying for jobs, but without any leads. I was applying for jobs ranging from fast food work to research positions, and was never called to interview. When I asked employers what I could do to improve myself as a candidate, I was repeatedly told I was over-qualified for fast food and underqualified for jobs that required my degree. We began to panic as our bank account dwindled into nothing, and I clung to the possibility of my art developing into a financially sustaining career. There was no other option.

Within a year, my art business was, in fact, doing well, but not well enough to make anything close to a living wage. I was still unsuccessful in finding traditional work. We were living in a coastal town whose booming economy was reflected in its housing market. Our apartment rent was raised more than one hundred dollars, and we couldn't afford to stay. We were unable to find cheaper housing, and we couldn't convince any family members to let us stay with them for a few weeks while we figured out our situation. Within the month we were without a place to live. In a panic, having nothing but a few belongings in our car, we decided to move to our favorite vacation spot, East Tennessee. If there was ever a time to take a risk and a leap of faith, it was now because we literally had nothing to lose. In Tennessee, we found affordable housing, and we both found work. I forced myself to work part-time running all daily operations—from phones to treatments—for a local alternative therapy business until we were stable enough or until my art business earned more than my job.

As we settled into our new apartment and our new life in East Tennessee, our marriage was flourishing. Emotionally, we were still best friends and despite the hardship of our finances, we were happy together. We were having sex multiple times a week—even multiple times a day during ovulation, just to see if we could get pregnant—and nothing. I opened my laptop, afraid to search for what I was about to type. How long does it take to get pregnant? Searching page after page, reading facts and research, I learned that most people get pregnant in three months; that, for some people, it might take six months; and that for those who had tried for over a year, without conceiving, there was a problem.

My heart sank as I realized we were infertile, and I knew it was my fault. While there was no proof that I was to blame, I knew without a doubt that this inability to conceive was just another unexplainable issue. On some level, I wasn't surprised at the internet diagnosis; I had a feeling all along that we would never have kids. We'd had quite a few years of using no contraception and had experienced a miscarriage. Pregnancy wasn't supposed to be this evasive.

The guilt of knowing I was infertile hit me hard, harder than I expected. At this point, I wasn't even as concerned about not having a child as I was about not being able to provide my husband with a family. Would he have still married me had he known I was unable to have kids? Would we have to resort to in-vitro fertilization (IVF)? We had always talked about having kids one day. Was it a marriage-ender if I couldn't? My mind was spinning as I remembered all of the Ob-gyn visits years ago, the strange periods, and the bizarre issues I had always experienced.

Living in Tennessee, I struggled to find my place in what appeared to be a non-diverse, conservative town. Tennessee was the opposite of the liberal beach town where I grew up. At work, I often encountered this difference in cultural attitudes as I spoke with customers. One example was an elderly man who came into the shop regularly. Although he was incredibly sweet, he was beyond nosy.

"So, why are you working and haven't had any kids yet?" he asked bluntly.

"Oh . . . Well, just making ends meet and I'm sure we will have kids one day," I replied, trying to avoid conflict.

"Are you on birth control?"

"No," I replied honestly, shocked that he felt he had a right to ask about my reproductive choices.

"When the lord is ready for you to have children, it will come," he smiled and nodded as I pretended to clean something in the other room, desperately trying to escape any question about fertility or religious conversation with a customer.

I assumed that this man's overly personal remarks must have just been a fluke — until a well-educated woman came into the shop one day. As I was assisting her, she sparked up a conversation.

"You should really get yourself some education, honey. That way you won't have to work customer service forever," she patted my hand as I walked by, taking notice of my wedding ring.

"Oh, actually I have a bachelor's in biological science, with a minor in American Sign Language, as well as an associates in arts," I smiled back at her. "Graduated a while back now."

"Ah, sorry. So how many kids do you have?"

"None," I said, turning my back to answer the phone that wasn't ringing.

"Better get on that before he leaves you," she retorted.

Again, I concluded that the culture here was just different. These people's opinions didn't matter to me. They didn't know what I was going through or that I had tried to have children. It wasn't their fault that I was so sensitive. While their comments bothered me, none of their remarks left a lasting impression until one of the patrons with whom I had established a friendship mentioned his wife.

His wife had a child but was struggling to conceive her second. They had tried for months and she wasn't pregnant. This man continued to share his disappointments and hopes with me. Eventually, he explained, he and his wife learned that she ovulated only once every few months and that with hCG shots to release multiple eggs, they'd be fine. He teared up with the hope of having a second child, yet I worried about his poor wife who must have felt like a pin cushion.

"So, I know I ask you all the time, but why haven't you had kids, yet?" he asked, eyes glossy from the heaviness of our conversation.

"I—" I started to make an excuse, but after hearing the candid emotion in his own story and imagining what my own husband must be feeling, I broke. "We can't have kids."

"Oh, my god. And I've been asking you all the time when you are going to. God damn it, I am such an asshole, and all this time, your face . . . You told me, without telling me," he stammered, walking over to me. Standing there sobbing in front of him, I felt so vulnerable. So weak.

"Do you know why?" he asked, handing me paper towels from the stack behind the desk.

"No. They don't know," I replied.

It was the first time I had ever spoken out loud about my infertility. The first time I had ever admitted to anyone that I was struggling with something so sensitive.

After understanding this man's feelings as perhaps being similar to my husband's, and after months of endless talks with my husband about his feelings, I felt as if we came to a kind of acceptance about the possibly of not being able to have children. Despite accepting our fate, my husband encouraged me to see a doctor to make sure nothing else was wrong. Unfortunately, though, we still couldn't afford health insurance, and there was no way I was going to let another Ob-gyn get near me again. So, I let time pass by and ignored the steadily increasing pain. Infertilely sucked, but I got over it.

By now, at twenty-three, I had spent over a decade of my life plagued by periods that were painful and often irregular. The disabling pain continued, and I was used to dealing with the frequent dizziness. A troubling new development, though, was that sex was becoming more unbearable. It was, at the least, uncomfortable, and at times it was excruciating. But as time passed, with every penetration, I felt like I was being stabbed and ripped open. There was no reasonable explanation for the sharp stabbing sensation I was feeling.

At first, I just assumed the worsening pain that accompanied sex was due to the stress that came with relocating to a different state and starting our lives anew. Gradually, though, I started to second-guess myself, contemplating whether my body or my psyche was causing the pain. Maybe I just didn't want to have sex. No. I definitely wanted to have sex. So, then what? Maybe I just didn't want to have sex with my husband. I felt a wave of guilt for even having the thought. My husband is one of the most compassionate and understanding people I have known, and I was madly in love with him; perhaps more importantly, he was my best friend. I was reluctant to even consider the possibility that maybe I had just grown tired of sex with him, and I continued to struggle with the question of whether the pain was caused by my body or my mind. After much reflection and self-questioning, I knew one thing to be true. I knew the issue lay in my body, because my mind was still madly in love with him.

The pain slowly evolved over the following year. I was now twenty-four. The pelvic aching lengthened from two weeks to three weeks, and eventually there were no pain-free days. Sharp pains seemed to strike me like random stabs of a dagger into my ovaries, while also twisting my stomach. Sex was a nightmare, and, by now, even being turned on started to hurt; I felt the aching and swelling feeling simply by thinking about sex. It was one thing to give up vaginal penetration, but to give up any sort of pleasure for myself or for my husband was beyond sexually frustrating. I began trying to still take part in sex physically, while keeping my mind as disconnected as I possible; even then, my body reacted negatively, despite my attempt to disassociate my mind. Even tampons started to cause significant pain, and I was unable to use even the smallest of them during my cycle.

Another new symptom to emerge during this time was that I always seemed to be having either diarrhea or constipation, and it began to hurt to defecate. I could anticipate a bowel movement a few hours in advance because of the stabbing sensation in my intestines. The more I used my muscles, the more it felt like I was having anal sex with a pinecone. My neighbors must have been able to hear the screaming as I sat on the toilet, trying to do the simple task of passing a bowel movement. They were so painful, I debated going to the hospital, but ultimately decided to avoid the bill and saline drip. After all, nothing was ever done for me before. Even when I urinated, my stomach felt as if it were going to implode from the pain. My body began to hurt to sit, to stand, to sleep, and I had begun waking up—to my own crying—at three in the morning every night. The heating pad never left my stomach to the point where the skin on my stomach started to burn, leaving marks for days. At this point it was clear that I needed to face my fears and see an Ob-gyn, eventually.

Living in bed was my new normal. I was afraid to tell my friends or my family about the severity of my symptoms because doctors still could not figure it out. How could I begin to tell someone I was experiencing such extreme pain, yet there was no medical cause for it.

I had been in bed for days, and my art business was waiting on me to work. I had to get up and paint customers' orders. I couldn't afford to refund their payments, and if I left their orders unpainted, I'd destroy my business and reputation. Deciding to go to my in-home studio, I slowly made my way to my desk. A wave of dizziness overcame me, and I fell to the floor. Nausea along with the familiar gut punches, ensued, and I reached for a nearby pencil box, vomiting into the container. I tried to stand up, to even move, but I couldn't. Over an hour later, I was finally able to reach for my phone, lying on the desk above me, to call my husband home. Waiting for him to come home and carry me to bed, I was on the floor for hours, unable to move, and on the verge of blacking out. I felt ready for my life to end. Living like this, wasn't living.

I spent the following weeks in bed, cursing my pain, hating the fact that I was a woman—and, worst of all, according to a family member in whom I had confided about the infertility, a "biologically broken" one. My psyche was cracking, and I wrote a suicide note to my husband because I knew that I could not live the rest of my life in pain without knowing that there was a cause or reason for it. I would not end my life without reason; however, I knew that living my life in this amount of pain had only one outcome. There would be a day when I wouldn't be strong enough to keep fighting my undiagnosable enemy.

Although I had vowed to never visit another Ob-gyn, I did decide to make an appointment with a new general practitioner who prescribed anxiety medication that I did not want or need. Assuming my symptoms were caused by stress, he had hoped the anxiety medication would help with the dizziness and fainting. I also visited a new endocrinologist and a new neurologist, both of whom ordered an array of diagnostic tests. The results of each test were the same as before: no cause was found for the fatigue, pain, nausea, fainting, or dizziness. These doctors prescribed a plethora of medications for prevention. I took none of them, though, as I was not suffering from potential medical issues, from but crippling pain. Taking preventative medicine for a problem that didn't yet exist seemed idiotic. The most frustrating part of these doctors' visits was that each appointment ended with the doctors asking my husband what he did for a living. Upon hearing his response, they looked at me, confused.

"If you have no kids, then what do you do?" they would say, as if a woman's only option was to be an incubator.

"I'm an artist," I always said, as they smiled.

"Ah! An artist . . ." they replied with such a smug arrogance, as if they really meant to say, "Ah, a childless housewife."

Not long after these futile doctors' appointments, I was bed bound again, watching a revamp of one of my favorite shows from the late eighties. One of the show's characters, who was like a mom figure, was talking to one of the now-grown daughters about her new found infertility problems. They discussed the reality that having an answer, no matter how heartbreaking that answer may be, is better than not knowing. She was right. I needed to keep looking for answers, just in case the cause was something stupid. Crying through the episode, I called my husband at work and babbled about wanting to know what was causing the infertility. It was time to face my fears and seek answers.

Thanks to a fictional character, I started to gain the confidence to look into my problems. I searched the internet for a fertility specialist in my town, looked over the cost of treatments, and immediately came to the decision that I would never be able to afford fertility treatment. Subsequently, I talked with adults who had gone through the adoption process as children and with parents who had adopted. These conversations helped me realize that I needed to be in a much more stable environment before I could even begin the adoption process. I had so much to learn, and I knew I wasn't ready to merge our family with another and care for a child who would need unprecedented support and understanding. Again, the process was expensive, and I felt overwhelmed and discouraged.

I started to evaluate why I was so intent on the idea of having a baby. My husband and I had come to the understanding that we didn't need children. But I wasn't completely sure, and seeing his eyes light up when he saw a child in a store also made me question his feelings about having a child. Did I want to have a child because of cultural expectations? Was it because having children was what I had always thought I was supposed to do with my life? Or was it maybe because I wanted to see a little re-creation of my husband and me? Was it to be able to experience being pregnant? Did I want to have children for my husband? Was it because I wanted to create and sustain a life — giving the child everything they deserved and being a supportive force behind them? Maybe it was because members of both our families made me feel like I was inferior because another I hadn't yet produced another human being. My mind was spinning, but, eventually, I let the idea go again. I wasn't going to see an Ob-gyn. I couldn't afford fertility treatments and wasn't mentally ready to go through the adoption process, so I was in no shape to be a mother.

I was continuing with my life and was now twenty-five. The pain continued, still without a diagnosed cause. The pain was going to kill me, or I would. Financially, my husband and I were finally in a better place, and we had excellent health insurance; still, I was afraid to repeat the endless cycle of doctor visits. Despite my husband's encouragement, I didn't want to go. I had a thriving business that required my attention twenty-four seven, and that was all I was going to focus on.

Later that year, in December, I was working in my art studio with the television on in the background. As I heard a commercial come across the speaker, I started to pay more attention. A woman was telling her Ob-gyn that she had been having cramps that felt like stabbing knives, and she was explaining everything that I had been feeling and experiencing. There was a name for her problem, but I wasn't able to turn up the sound in time to catch it. A few days later, the commercial came on again, and, excitedly, I called out for my husband to come over to the television. We both watched in shock as she described pain with sex, stabbing pains, literally everything I had struggled with — she was naming every symptom. This commercial had to be representing my illness! I cried from the excitement of realizing that my symptoms were explainable and laughed because I related to one of those silly ads. But more than anything, I was terrified. What the hell was this thing called endometriosis?

CHAPTER SIX

Fighting for Answers

*A*n awareness company created the commercial that started my itch for answers. I cannot thank the group enough for sponsoring this commercial that changed my life. If I had not seen it, I may have never known what endometriosis is; without this knowledge, I could have ultimately succumbed to the depression that resulted from being in constant pain. This short commercial gave me hope.

I visited the awareness website for more information, and my eyes quickly jumped to the sentence, "There is no cure." Terrified to read further, I closed the browser, too afraid to look into the treatments. I didn't want to know more; I wasn't going to be one of those people who self-diagnosed based on an ad or a random website. Sure, the symptoms sounded like mine, but if I really did have endometriosis and there really wasn't a cure, then I would continue to ignore my pain for as long as I could. Every time the commercial came on, my husband urged me to make an appointment with the Ob-gyn. I explained to him that endometriosis was just a fearsome disease with no cure and that I didn't want anything to do with the illness. He assured me that there must be a treatment or a cure for a disease that affects so many people. Maybe I didn't even have endo, he pointed out, but he did want me to see a doctor.

A week later, another bout of extreme pain left me bedridden for an entire seven days, causing a major crash in sales for my business. That was the tipping point. I had to figure it out. I was unable to work at a traditional job, and I had found a way to accommodate that challenge—but if I couldn't even work for myself, then I had a problem. I made an appointment with a female Ob-gyn this time and prayed that since she was a woman, she might understand the unbelievable pain. I was ready to meet with her after researching endometriosis endlessly. Through my understanding of symptoms and the disease, I realized the dizziness that I had been experiencing was attached to the severe amounts of pain. All of my symptoms finally started to click and connect to the original problem I faced at eleven years old. I had a bit of an understanding of endometriosis, and I just needed a great doctor to help me figure out the next steps.

In choosing a woman doctor, I wanted to make sure that she could viscerally relate when I told her my ovaries felt as if were being stabbed, pinched, and twisted. When I explained that the sensation felt like a bomb with ninja stars was repetitively going off in my uterus, I hoped she could comprehend that this was more than typical cramps. Besides, after my last experience, I wasn't ready to see a male Ob-gyn.

I called to make the appointment and was scheduled for the earliest available time, which, unfortunately, was a three-month wait. I was so excited when the appointment day finally came; we arrived at the office thirty minutes early. Once inside, though, we realized we were at the sister office, and that my appointment was at the downtown office, about forty minutes away. We rushed to get downtown, but I was ten minutes late and they had already canceled the appointment. The receptionist explained that I could either sit in the waiting room for the next six hours or come back again in three months. I chose to stay and wait until the Ob-gyn could see me in at the end of the day.

When I finally met with the doctor, I explained my entire story to her, from my first period until now. Thankfully, she was more than understanding. I told her that we had hoped to have the option of having kids one day. I was careful not to mention the word "endometriosis"; I wanted her to tell me I had the illness and that I wasn't crazy for believing I had this disease because of a commercial I related to.

I also explicitly told her that I didn't want to be on birth control because of the adverse reaction I'd had to it. Still uneducated about my condition and my options, I speculated that I was likely to have IVF treatments for infertility and, eventually, a hysterectomy to alleviate the pain. I was ready to accept this course of treatment because I knew I didn't have many choices. To my surprise, the doctor prescribed me hormones to take daily, assuring me that the hormones were not birth control and that they would help eliminate pain. She smiled and explained that after a few months to a year of taking the hormones, I would be able to have a baby if we wanted one and the pain should be gone. My husband and I were happy with the doctor's prognosis, and I was amazed that there were hormones I could take that weren't actually birth control. I had never heard of this treatment and was excited to try something new. I felt like I was heard by the doctor. Better yet, she didn't think I was infertile, just off balance.

The hormone medication that she prescribed to balance me and "wake up" my fertility was called Lo Loestrin Fe. Despite my hopeful optimism, after I took the first pill, I bled continuously, and, to my shock, the pain I had been experiencing doubled. In addition, I had strange side effects like extreme headaches and mood swings, leaving me with the unstable feeling I used to experience while on birth control. Yet again, I was bed-bound most of the time, able to get work done only one or two days out of the week.

After about a month of taking the hormones, I decided to research what the hell I was putting in my body. Research lead me to the website for the medication. According to www.loloestrin.com, it is a low-dose birth control pill that is effective at preventing pregnancy and contains two types of female hormones: an estrogen called ethinyl estradiol and a progestin called norethindrone acetate. I scrolled down to read the side effects: "the most common side effects reported by women taking Lo Loestrin Fe in a study were nausea/vomiting, headache, spotting or bleeding between menstrual periods, painful menstruation, weight change, breast tenderness, acne, abdominal pain, anxiety, and depression."

Anger filled my soul. I couldn't wrap my mind around why the doctor would have prescribed a birth control pill that would prevent pregnancy in order to help eliminate my pain and allow me to become pregnant. For that matter, why would she prescribe a medication whose side effects included nonstop bleeding, even worse pain during menstruation, more abdominal pain, nausea, and headaches — especially when I had specifically told her I did not want to be on birth control. What made this worse is that I was lied to, again.

Fuming, I called the doctor's office and told the assistant that something was wrong. A few days later, I got a call back from the doctor's assistant, who assured me that my symptoms were normal, but that we would do more tests. I just had to give the medicine six months to normalize. I took a deep breath, against my better judgment, decided to give it a shot. The pain was too much to deal with, and I was open to trying anything that could give me my life back.

After three months on the medication, I was back in the doctor's office, and I refused to continue taking the pills. The results of my recent tests showed a regular pap smear and a clear sonogram. I described to the doctor how I could always feel the pain in my ovaries, as if needles were being stabbed into them, or as if they were being squished between the fingers of a giant. She assured me the sensation was completely normal, that all women could feel similar sensations in their ovaries. During the internal sonogram, the pain had been so unbearable that I had almost punched the nurse as I lay there crying. The nurse assured me the sonogram was uncomfortable for everyone. Yet, I hadn't been just uncomfortable; I had been in so much pain that I could have sworn the wand was a branding iron. I had undergone an internal sonogram many times before, and never had it felt anything like this.

CHAPTER SIX

I told the doctor, then, that the pain with sex had to change. I was tired of being aroused and then crying from the pain, unable to have any sexual freedom because my body was preventing me from doing so. She responded by explaining that I was likely projecting a negative past experience onto the current situation, and that I needed to try to be more present. The truth was, I did have a history of sexual abuse, and so I thought maybe she was right. I could be bringing up old pain and causing myself to believe I just wasn't comfortable. Yet, I knew I had healed from those situations, and I knew I was safe in my marriage. I had already questioned myself about the possibility of psychic pain a year or so ago, and I had worked through the self-discovery of learning what I wanted—and it was still my husband. I knew this wasn't all in my head.

Frustrated with yet another doctor writing off my pain, I asked her if she thought I had endometriosis, finally saying the word out loud. She told me I was too young to have the disease (this is entirely false, though I did not know it at the time), and I took her word for it. She was doubtful that I had endo, she said, but we would still try to stop the pain for the time being.

We switched to a lower dose of birth control, and, at this point, I was fine with not having children. The doctor explained that my options were having kids but being in pain forever, or eliminating my pain but potentially not having kids. I opted to get rid of the pain. The doctor started me on norethindrone, which, according to my good friend, the internet, was commonly used in treatment for endometriosis! Aha! So she did think I had this incurable disease. At this point, I needed to figure out what the hell endometriosis was, and I immersed myself in research articles, Facebook support groups, and watched every YouTube Storytime on the subject.

My heart sank as I further researched endometriosis. Several documents said that ten percent of people assigned female at birth have endo, and a local fertility doctor's research showed that women experiencing infertility have a fifty percent chance of having endometriosis. I was a woman and experiencing infertility, so there was a substantial chance I had it; yet, for some reason, my Ob-gyn didn't

48

think so. The more I listened to women's experiences recounted across the internet, the more empowered I felt in believing that I did share the illness with them. As I read information and research, and listened to story after story, I began to realize that I now knew more about endometriosis than my doctor did.

The norethindrone was better than Lo Loestrin Fe, but it caused violent mood swings, and I experienced more anger than I had ever experienced in my life. I was spotting heavily throughout the three months I took the tablets. I did have less cramping than I did while on Lo Loestrin Fe, but it wasn't worth the trade-off to have slightly less cramping, but non-stop spotting and daily rages instead. I stopped taking the pill and made yet another appointment with the Ob-gyn. I felt like I was sixteen again, taking all of these medications with no hope of any relief.

At my next appointment, I felt like I had gathered enough information to ask the doctor, point-blank, about endo. I knew I needed answers, and I knew I needed them quickly because the pain was so severe that I was always agitated, ready to lash out at everyone around me. I knew by now that the only way endo can be diagnosed was with laparoscopy, and I came into the doctor's office determined to schedule the surgery.

The Ob-gyn was frustrated that I refused to take the norethindrone for a full six months, just as I had refused to take Lo Loestrin Fe for a full six months. I told her that my pain had not improved at all from the pre-birth control pain levels. In fact, the pain had intensified. I had even begun developing a sizeable swollen stomach that resembled a pregnancy belly that would appear in as little as ten minutes after eating.

"I really think I have endometriosis," I said, lying on the table as she pressed around my uterus.

"Does this hurt?" she asked.

"Yes," I winced over and over again, annoyed because I had already told her my cramps were so painful that my husband had to practically carry me into the office.

"Well," she paused, sitting across the room, "the only way to di-

agnose endometriosis would be a diagnostic laparoscopic surgery,"
confirming what I had read online, she continued, "I would say there
is only about a thirty-percent chance that you have endo. You are
young, and it typically doesn't show up like this."

I rolled my eyes, thinking about how so many of the storytime
videos were from women who finally got answers at about my age,
in their twenties—the age when they were old enough to figure out
the pain. Sure, it could pop up at any age, but for people who had
dealt with it since their first period, like I had, all had the same story
as mine.

"Doing laparoscopy wouldn't be my choice," the doctor stated,
looking directly into my eyes. "If you are going to be this insistent,
then we can do exploratory surgery to see if it is there. I would then
finish the surgery and we would discuss it about a month later to go
over your results and our next steps of treatment. However, I don't
think that is the case here. What I really feel you are dealing with
is something called a positive-feedback loop. So, because you really
have been believing that you have endometriosis mentally, you are
convincing yourself that you are feeling that pain," she smiled and
left the room.

I looked at my husband shocked, at a pure loss for words. The
doctor had just accused me of feeling like I have endometriosis and
imagining that I am experiencing the symptoms, such as pain with
sex, daily cramps, fatigue, and severe pelvic pain. What she had described, in reference to a person's mental state, is called anhedonia a
mood disorder which is said to reduce one's motivation and ability
to experience pleasure. According to Blood-Spinal Cord and Brain
Barriers in Health and Disease, 2004 other diseases that are often associated with anhedonia include PTSD, Schizophrenia, and major
depressive disorder.

My mouth dropped, as I went to pay the office visit fee. I walked
out feeling defeated. The Ob-gyn had gotten into my head before,
suggesting that I was having pain because I didn't want to have sex.
I knew that was completely false. Now she was claiming that I was
having pain because I thought I had endo? I didn't even realize that

endo existed until six months ago! There was no way this was all in my head. We ended the appointment with the plan that if I was still experiencing pain within the next three months, we could meet again to discuss potentially doing laparoscopic exploratory surgery.

There was no way in hell I would allow this woman to cut into me, as she wouldn't recognize endo if the excised tissue were held in front of her face. I continued doing further research and discovered that there are very wrong ways to treat endo, as well as a current gold standard. I came across a Facebook group called Nancy's Nook Endometriosis Education; apparently, it was a life-changing group, and I had to know what it was all about.

I soon learned that this group is like an endometriosis textbook. Within its posts and links, I found a list of Gold Standard doctors. These doctors have high standards of care and impressive success rates, and they use the surgical technique of excision, the only recommended way to treat endo. Excision is a procedure in which doctors remove lesions, sometimes several tissue layers deep. The goal of excision is to remove the endometriosis without harming the healthy tissue around it. I also read that some women had several unsuccessful surgeries using a procedure called ablation. In this procedure, the doctor does not entirely cut out the lesions but burns them at a surface level, often leaving parts of the lesions buried deeper in the tissue behind.

Originally I had thought that a hysterectomy would be an option, but it was explained to me that just as vines on a tree can grow again after the tree is a stump, endo can grow back after the uterus is removed. Endo can exist throughout our bodies, from our ovaries to even our ears, nose, and brain, in rare cases. It can affect people of all genders; in rare cases, people who are assigned male at birth. However, with excision—cutting and removing as much endo as possible—there is a much higher chance that the endo will not return; it is the method chosen by the most advanced experts in endometriosis treatments today.

Through Facebook group recommendations as well as research on a few specialists, I found a doctor roughly two hours away from me.

CHAPTER SIX

I made an appointment to meet with him; another three-month wait, but I had to do it. Waiting for this appointment was grueling, and on the day of the meeting, I was in so much pain that I wasn't sure I could survive the two-hour car ride. Thankfully, upon our arrival, the medical staff members were amazing, and to my greatest relief, they listened.

Meeting with the doctor, I told him my story. Immediately, he replied that he thought I have endo; he said that there was no way it was in my head, but in my pelvis. I will forever remember those words, and after the appointment I cried from the shock and relief of being told that an endo professional believed I had the disease. That day, we scheduled my surgery for the soonest possible date, the week of my twenty-sixth birthday — still another two months away.

Surgery

The three-month wait for surgery felt like being in purgatory: endless waiting for the savior of excision. So many people claimed that their pain was eliminated, or nearly eliminated for at least a few years after excision by a specialist. Yet, I had panic attacks as I worried about complications during surgery, about what I would do if the surgery didn't help, and about what I would do if I didn't have endo. All of these negative thoughts plagued me between the nonstop pain that left me unable to walk any farther than the mailbox at the end of my driveway for months.

I finally decided to tell my family. Even some of them doubted that I really had endo, thinking that I was extreme in opting for the surgery to diagnose and treat my condition. A few family members chattered about how I would finally be able to produce a spawn they could all carelessly coo about from another state. Other close family members never even spoke to me about endo or my surgery, and they never wished me well, instead pretending as if I was just being dramatic. My heart hurt to know that those I had loved were still skeptical about an illness that had existed throughout my medical history since I was eleven.

CHAPTER SEVEN

My period started the week of surgery, amplifying my pain even further. I knew the universe hated me, and this was its way of giving me the middle finger. I kept reminding myself that excision was a treatment, not a cure. I would still be a woman battling endo. Even with the affected areas removed from my body, the endo could come back. I may be in this exact situation once again. The realization that I had a chronic illness that I would battle for the rest of my life was overwhelming.

Surgery was one day away, and I was required to fast for twenty-four hours before the procedure and stop liquids eight hours before. I was also instructed to do a fleet enema in order to prepare my bowels (one of the strangest feelings I hope never to experience again). Finally, surgery day arrived, and I was so grateful because my pain had hit yet another peak. No matter what happened as a result of the surgery, the outcome had to be better than this.

My husband and I woke up at four in the morning, with the car packed the night before. I kissed all three cats and our dog goodbye before my husband helped me into the car, ready for the two-hour drive to the hospital. As he drove, we joked along the way, finding our way to the center of the city, where the hospital spanned several blocks. We checked in and were quickly led to a room where hospital staff started blood work and then asked me to change into a hospital gown. Although I wasn't able to wear underwear during surgery, I was given charming mesh panties, with a cardboard-like pad to wear. It was a fight to get them, but, ultimately, I had to tell the nurse that it was either the panties and pad, or cleaning up menstrual blood.

My husband took my wedding band, placing it halfway up his pinky finger. He spun around in the hospital recliner, joking about anything and everything in order to ease my sheer panic. We waited an hour before a nurse came to take me back to surgery prep. Kissing my husband goodbye, I swallowed hard, hoping he would see the message I texted to him thank him for support throughout our lives together, even if it turned out that I didn't have endo.

The nurse pushed my hospital gurney through a labyrinth of

hallways to a surgical prep area. Nurse after nurse entered the area, placing an IV into my arm, clipping a heart monitor on my finger, and attaching pads and other pieces of equipment all over me, as I listened to the chatter of the other patients and doctors. Each time a nurse walked past, I heard my heart monitor speed up. Trying to stop the rapid beeping, I stared at the blank wall in front of me and focused on nothing but the wall's muted blue color until the beeping slowed. Finally, a woman stopped in front of me and, in a voice that seemed cracked from years of smoking, told me I was ready to go. She fumbled through my papers clumsily, her hair escaping from a ponytail and sticking out in random clumps.

"You're my girl! Ready to go? I'm gonna get yeh ready now."

Despite living in Tennessee for three years, I was alarmed by the exaggerated country accent paired with the woman's disheveled demeanor. I felt like I was about to enter a slaughterhouse, and I still hadn't seen my doctor. I heard the beeping of my heart monitor accelerate.

"Wait . . . Y'er Bethany?" she asked, wrinkles of confusion covering her face.

"Yes," I said, watching her flip my file in circles, squinting as she read the pages.

"Holy moly! Look at all that stuff they are gonna be doin' to yeh. Yer not the girl I was looking for." She slammed the file on the table in front of me and walked a few beds over.

My heart pounded as she walked over to another girl.

"You're my girl! Ready to go? I'm gonna get yeh ready now!" she repeated to someone else, as she laughed about mistaking that girl for me.

I desperately wished I had my phone so that I could tell my husband that I was terrified the hospital was this unorganized. The other girl was wheeled back through the doors, as the nurse chatted away beside her bed.

"And that's why I still live with my no-good, cheating, lying husband. Sorry, ex-husband! I have a divorce in the makin's, so we ain't married in my book—and I told em, he ain't gonna be livin' with me once I get a raise."

"Oh. Nice," the terrified girl managed to say as she disappeared behind the doors.

A few minutes later, my anesthesiologist, and his nurse came up to introduce themselves. They were gracious and helpful, covering me with warm blankets. My primary nurse came by, and, she, too, was sweet and attentive while we went over my medical history for the millionth time before I finally saw my doctor. My heart rate slowed down as I took a deep breath.

The excision specialist was in an optimistic mood and reassured me that I was in the right place, and that we were good to go. The nurse injected me with the first set of anesthesia medications to calm me down. As we entered the surgery room, the world was quiet and, despite the many machines. The nurse told me that DaVinci would be the robot that would be doing the excision. Thanks, DaVinci. I climbed onto the table, mentioned something about the disappoint-ing ending of a widely popular fantasy television series, and that was the last thing I remember.

I felt myself awake, my fingers tracing a tube along the cheek of my face, following it to my nose. An oxygen tube. I felt tape being pulled off of my ear and heard the nurse mention something about a monitor being taken off. It was over.

"Did I have endo?" The first post-surgery words escaped my mouth, as my eyes took in the pale, blurred colors of the room around me.

"We don't know," someone replied.

Moments or hours passed, I couldn't be sure. I was exhausted and frustrated. Why didn't they know? Where was the doctor? Did I do all of this for nothing? I blinked hard, trying to see, but the room was still a pale white-and-blue blur, as I heard the moans of other patients coming out of surgery. My eyes shut.

"Keep breathing!" a nurse yelled as I gasped air into my lungs, realizing the oxygen tube was no longer there.

"Did they find endometriosis?" I asked the nurse, but his response was the same as the last. They didn't know. I felt hot tears slipping down onto my cheeks, and I knew I was crying.

"Why are you crying?" another nurse asked.

"I can't feel the endo pain, I'm in pain, but I don't feel endo any-more."

"What did she say?" a third nurse asked.

"She's crying because she doesn't feel endo pain." the nurse scoffed.

I didn't even care whether or not they knew if I had endo. I knew I did, and I knew at that very moment because I felt better. Maybe it was the drugs, or perhaps the anesthesia, but I wholeheartedly felt like the pain and swelling from my stomach was no longer there. My eyes closed.

"Keep breathing!" The nurse shook me awake again. Immediately, I started asking for water, for my husband, for someone who could tell me about the surgery.

Two hours passed before I was moved to a patient room. I was still incredibly dizzy and unable to see clearly as my gurney was wheeled into the main hospital. I opened my eyes to see the blur of a hallway passing by me. I thought I saw my husband, then again, then again. Each time I would have sworn he was there, but he wasn't. Where was he? I wondered if he knew if I had endo or not. I wondered if he knew if I was awake and out of surgery.

Not long after I was settled in my room, a nurse came in and in-structed me to pee. There was no way I could stand, let alone make it to the ensuite bathroom. I focused my eyes and glimpsed at the nurse, a woman who was shorter than me and strikingly thin. I knew she would be unable to support my dead weight. I didn't want to offend her, but there was no logical way she could do it.

"You won't be able to support me. I'm dizzy, and I can't stand," I warned.

Did I have to pee, yes; could I get there, no. She told me that if I wanted my husband to know I was in the room, I would need to uri-nate first. Angry and wanting to see him, I tried to stand, the muscles of my stomach straining to find strength. Just as I felt my feet touch the floor, the nurse quickly dropped me onto the bed, causing every incision to twinge in pain. I silently cursed at her.

"Get my husband now!" I roared, annoyed that she hadn't listened to my warning.

She left quickly, blaming me for slamming myself down into the bed. I rolled my eyes as I lifted the stiff cotton gown to look down at my stomach for the first time. My eyes took in the incisions — one; two; my belly button was another, three; four; a hole near my ribs; and a tube going into my body a few inches below my navel. What the hell was that? I examined my hands and arms, counting over eleven needle holes where nurses clearly had trouble trying to hit a vein.

Blinking hard toward the doorway I smiled as my husband came into the room. I wanted to hug him, to tell him about the crazy nurse who had just dropped me and the crazier one who mixed me up with the other girl before surgery. I wanted to tell him that I loved him and that I hated the few dramatic hours without him, but that isn't what came out of my mouth.

"Did they find endo?" I asked him.

"Of course. Did you not see the doctor?" He asked me.

"No. No one has told me anything yet. What happened?" I wanted to know everything.

"He said it was everywhere and embedded throughout your body really deep. Are you feeling okay?"

Smiling with relief, as twisted as it sounds, I was so happy that I had received a diagnosis. I started telling him about the crazy experiences I had, and then about the amazing nurses who gave me warm blankets and I tried to recount as much as I could from the past several hours. My husband helped me into the bathroom, and by the time I came out, my bed had been removed from my room. I was processed to be discharged from the hospital and able to go home.

We started our two-and-a-half-hour ride home. My husband stopped to get me food, though I ate only three bites before I was full. The bumps in the road were brutal, but to take my mind off of the discomfort, I designed a few book covers, posted an update on social media, and wasn't feeling half bad! Time was a blur, but soon

I was home and eating a delicious spinach wrap my husband made me for dinner. I was already more productive than I had been in the past few months.

I had been told to take a laxative with each meal, and by the next day, I was vomiting and had nonstop diarrhea for fourteen hours. I called the doctor, who told me to go to the ER and have a CAT scan to ensure that everything was okay. After several hours in the hospital, I was cleared and given fluids and a strong anti-nausea medication. I felt much better afterward and made it through the second day. The third day was miserable. On the fourth, I was able to pull the tube out of my stomach and lose the pain pump I had been carrying around. My recovery progressed so much faster now that I was finally able to move without lugging around a bag of liquid, and I slept without worrying about pulling on the tube.

Before surgery I promised myself that my pain would be better after excision. I would feel nothing. Sure endo could grow back, but maybe it wouldn't. Perhaps I'd only have to have one surgery. Maybe the word endometriosis would be a bad memory of my young life and nothing more.

I did feel better immediately after surgery. Or at least I thought I had. It took a week for one of the sharp stabs of pain to return, piercing through my body. To feel the endo-like pain I never wanted to feel again. I wasn't sure if it was endo or healing pains. Feeling a hot salty tear run down my cheek, I realized that I had been creating a fantasy in my mind during the year I had been waiting for a cure.

That first week of my healing process was a blur of getting up and down, focusing on using the restroom, and sleeping. At the beginning of the second week, I finally started to feel better. I was able to move around much more and could start getting my life back in order. By the end of second week I felt nearly normal. I still experienced occasional sharp stabs from healing, or so I assumed, but not enough to take any more than a few acetaminophen every day or so.

I had been dreaming of my favorite foods. I knew that eating them increased my pain and inflammation, but if the endo was excised, maybe I was in the clear? So, I had a mouthful of extra cheesy mac and cheese and a soda. Not even five minutes later, my stomach swelled into the endo belly I hated, and I knew I would never escape endo, not even for a mere moment. I am a prisoner to this disease that wants to crush my spirit, and I will remain so until death. I have to keep fighting. I have to continue being a warrior. I have to keep searching for better ways to decrease the pain. I have to live. Surgery was simply one step of treating the pain.

Upset from this realization, I stumbled my way into the bathroom, lifting my large T-shirt to see my stomach. I had developed bruises there, around the area of the incisions, and I cried at the hideous marks this "invisible" disease left behind on my body. My husband walked into the bathroom and hugged me.

"Why are you crying?" he asked, kissing my head.

"My stomach…. it's horrible." I didn't want to see the scars every day as a reminder of the agonizing pain I have faced and will continue to face.

"What? Horrible? No. You should be smiling and showing them off! Those are your battle scars! Or did you forget that you were a badass warrior?" He smiled reassuringly.

He was right. I should be proud. I found answers despite the doctors I encountered along the way. Instead of recognizing a debilitating chronic illness that was affecting a woman's life these doctors told me for nearly fifteen years that I was weak; that my symptoms were hysterics; that it was a psychological problem I was projecting; that I needed to suck it up and be stronger; and that it was completely normal. I realized that endo was more than a disease. It was a gender inequality issue. These doctors' diagnoses always placed the blame on me instead of looking more deeply into my symptoms. Endo was named the "career woman's disease" in the eighties, a name that inherently blamed women for developing endometriosis because they were working and not bearing children. My scars aren't embarrassing, but empowering.

New Life

*S*ince surgery, I have been working towards regaining my sexual freedom, and have been experiencing less pain with sex than before; however, the pain can still excruciating at times. I've been improving this with yoga, pelvic floor exercises and continue to work towards having pain-free sex. A few months after surgery I am able to have pain-free sex! I am able to wear tampons without pain again. The pain and swelling is still present, but this something I have to work on with pelvic floor therapy and strengthen my muscles, learning to control and relax them. I highly recommend the use of magnetic dilators that are used to help relax your pelvic muscles for pain-free insertion. It was only after the use of these that I was able to have pain free sex for the first time in years.

I also discovered after the surgery that I have a second chronic illness called interstitial cystitis, which is often paired with endo. This condition makes my bladder feel like I have a UTI, with similar sensations of painful urination, need to urinate frequently, as well as pelvic pain. Since I know I have two conditions working against me,

CHAPTER EIGHT

I have to make sure I don't always blame endo. It isn't alone in causing the pain. Luckily, one of the best ways to keep treating both conditions is an anti-inflammatory diet (such as avoiding dairy, gluten, red meat, caffeine, trans fat) which I can say has been a tremendous help in decreasing my inflammation.

Once I was finally able to take a bath, after waiting for three weeks, I felt so much better again, being able to heat my core and melt away some of the pain. Using heat to help the pain is still one of my favorite methods of relief. Each day is a journey, and I have to focus on taking it one step at a time.

Ultimately I do believe the surgery helped. I assumed that a lot of the pain that returned after the first week was healing pains mimicking endo pains. However, after consulting with my specialist a few months later, it was confirmed that it was, in fact, endo pain. While I am still experiencing pain, it is remarkably better than it was before surgery. I would consider my discomfort mild to moderate, at times. I am able to walk, clean, and stretch, and I have gained mobility and freedom again. I also now know that expecting a cure from a treatment was a nice dream, but not a reality. Excision was step one in treatment. Step two is keeping a non-inflammation diet and finding new delicious meals. Step three will be keeping my body strong. It is important to keep my core, pelvis, and body active to help relieve pain and to use muscles that have been left unused or in pain for years. There will perhaps be more excision surgeries in the future as well. Lastly, I will keep spreading awareness and hoping for a deeper understanding of endometriosis, so that we can do more than live with endo — we can thrive.

While writing this book I am still in recovery, yet every single day is better than the one before. I am eating clean, trying hard not to give in to the cravings for food that cause inflammation, and every day it gets a little easier. I am becoming physically active and working hard to strengthen my core. I am becoming sexually active again while beating the fears of pain and learning to enjoy sex. Endometriosis has a silver lining. If it weren't for endo, I would have never become an artist, illustrator, or author, finding my true passion. Even despite the financial hardships this illness will cause throughout my life, endo has led me to live in a beautiful state, with new friends, in a city I love. While, yes, this illness is a daily burden, it has gifted me with some of the most beautiful moments of my life. Living each day and appreciating what I have, rather than lamenting what endo has taken from me, dramatically changed my view of living with this disease. I found answers. I am seeking treatments and, more than anything else, I am amongst a community of warriors.

Understanding Endometriosis

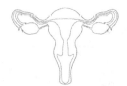

Talking about Endometriosis

*T*alking to your family is hard, but talking to your significant other is even harder. Throughout the past ten years with my husband, he has seen me get progressively worse, seen the symptoms amplify, and I think has helped him understand the crippling nature of endo. I couldn't imagine trying to explain this complex illness to someone I was just meeting.

The best way I can describe the pain endo causes is to liken it to that feeling of when you have to go to the bathroom so badly, and your stomach is twisting and punching—you don't know if you are going to explode from your bottom or top as the cold sweats start to happen. It is that awful feeling that makes you just pray to the universe that the suffering will end, but endo never does.

Some of my family members told me that I was biologically broken; they made me feel guilty for not having children, and they blame my husband and me for now choosing not have children. The key word is choosing. Now, after excision, I am supposedly fertile, but we have decided, since the choice is ours to make and not the disease choosing for us, that we choose to live our lives together as just the two of us. Science is showing an increase in evidence that endometriosis is hereditary and I couldn't pass endo onto my worst enemy.

Unfortunately, there are those people who will never understand. To that, my husband has said, "you have to understand that you can't understand," and I love that perspective. We, as endo warriors, have to be verbal to the people we love and let them know what we are feeling. But one of the first things you can do is educate them on endo. Give them resources to truly understand. One of the things that most helped my husband and me was reading story after story about women's experiences, and then relating their stories to my own. Endo is more than "period pain," and the difference between the two confuses a lot of people. Because endo is associated with menstrual periods, many people believe that endo just makes your life a little bumpier for a few days a month, when, in fact, it can affect you every second of every day, even waking you up at two in the morning, screaming in pain.

My family had the belief that one surgery would cure it all; that's a nice thought, but, in reality, there is no cure. While it can be exhausting to repeatedly tell the people you care about that there are only treatments, they are just hoping for the best for you. Explain to them that while you appreciate the positivity of their outlook, the reality is a lifelong battle between you and endometriosis. While you, too, are also hopeful that your treatments will lead to a pain-free lifestyle, you don't want to hear your loved ones' assurances that you will find a cure because that isn't yet possible. Continue to tell them that listening to assurances that you will find a cure can, in fact, cause depression when the heaviness of dealing with a chronic disease (that many people doubt you even have) weighs on your mind.

Be open to their questions and do your best not to get frustrated with the response. I know this is particularly tough if you are, like me, unable to be in the traditional workforce because of the enormous financial impact the disease has on your family. Living on just one a salary, along with endless medical bills, can lead to a lot of discontent; although your partner may be feeling overworked and stressed, explain that being in pain at home wasn't what you imagined for your life, either. You both are dealing with stressful situations, and, in my own experience, being open about your feelings can be one of the best ways to communicate with your partner, family and friends.

Don't be afraid to seek out professional help and reach out to support groups to talk with others who are experiencing similar situations. The community is enormous, and sometimes talking to others battling the same issues with their families can help you change the perspective of yours.

The Cost of Endometriosis

This section will vary significantly for every woman who deals with endo, however, for those in your life who like to look at numbers, I have complied my cost of endo, the best I could, within this past year (2018/19)

July-December:
- Initial Ob-gyn Visit: $200
- Pap-Smear & Bloodwork lab fees: $180
- Birth Control (used for treatment): $266 (cost for three months)
- Extra Tampons/Pads from non-stop bleeding: $60 (cost for three months of constant bleeding from prescribed birth control)
- Follow up Ob-gyn Visit: $200
- Ultrasound and transvaginal ultrasound: $400
- Over the counter meds: $100 (~$20 a month)
- Transportation cost + husband taking time off of work to help me go to visits because I was unable to walk

...or drive from the pain: $500

January-February:
- Ob-gyn Follow-up: $200
- Birth Control (used for treatment): $105 (cost for three months)
- Extra Tampons/Pads from non-stop bleeding: $60 (cost for three months of constant bleeding from pre-scribed birth control)
- Over the counter meds: $60 (~$20 a month)
- Sick Visit and Antibiotics Cost: $220 (when my immune system crashes around my period)
- Transportation cost + husband taking time off of work to help me go to visits because I was unable to walk or drive from the pain: $300

March-April:
- Initial Visit with Endo Specialist - $150 (Four hour round trip drive)
- Medication for pain while waiting for surgery - $100
- Over the counter meds: $40 (~20 a month)
- Transportation cost + husband taking time off of work - $240

May:
- Prescriptions for surgery - $4,321
- Laparoscopic Surgeon Bill - $3,946
- Anesthesiology during surgery - $2,522
- Radiology during surgery - $530
- Pathologist during surgery - $833 (Four hour round trip drive)
- Emergency Room Visit after surgery - $4,596
- Extra Tampons/Pads for bleeding after surgery and first extremely heavy period: $20
- Over the counter meds: $20

- Transportation cost + husband taking time off of work to take care of me during surgery - $640

June-July:
- Follow Up Visit with Endo Specialist - $150
    (Four hour round trip drive)
- Dilators for Pelvic Floor Therapy - $90
- Sick Visit and Antibiotics Cost: $220 (when my immune system crashes around my period)
- Sonogram and Transvaginal Sonogram - $400
- Over the counter meds: $40 (~20 a month)
- Transportation cost + husband taking time off of work - $240

Career Annual Salary: $40,000
(Career you are unable to have due to endo - this will vary by area/education/experience/hours you are able to work. A salary average from ZipRecruiter produced this number for my education and regional location)

Total Annual Loss on a surgery year: >$61,949
(This is without insurance considered. There are as many bills that I could find from the care I received in Tennessee. Some additional bills and costs are not included in this estimate. My specialist said on average their patients may have expert excision every five years)

Things that are priceless:
- Loss of time with family and friends
- Loss of career & hobbies
- Endless pain, suffering, and fatigue
- Emotional pain for ourselves and those affected

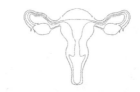

Definitions

ablation - a laparoscopic surgical procedure that burns endometrial lesions

adenomyosis - a painful condition caused by the inner lining of the uterus breaking through the muscle wall

birth control - commonly used to prevent pregnancy, however, it is also used for suppressing ovulation for painful periods bladder pain syndrome - the common name for interstitial cystitis

cervix - a narrow passage that forms the lower end of the uterus and connects to the vagina

chronic - persisting or recurring for an extended period of time

continuous birth control - when a doctor prescribes skipping the placebo pills, typically in three-month cycles, to reduce menstrual bleeding

depo-provera - a brand name for medroxyprogesterone acetate which is given as an injection to prevent your ovaries from releasing an egg by suppressing ovulation

dysmenorrhea - a medical term for painful periods

dyspareunia - a medical term for pain with sex

dilator - used to restore vaginal function for comfortable sexual activity

endo belly - a term to explain inflammation resulting in a swollen stomach

endocrine glands - secrete hormones into the bloodstream

endocrinologist - a medical professional that diagnoses and treats disorders of endocrine glands

endo diet - avoiding inflammation-causing foods such as red meat, dairy, gluten, trans fat, processed foods, and caffeine

endometriosis - a painful condition when tissue, similar to the tissue that lines the uterus (endometrium), grows in other places of the body outside of the uterus

endometrioma - a type of cyst that is formed from endometrial tissue growing in or on the ovaries

endometrium - innermost tissue that lines the uterus

excision - surgery to remove or destroy growths with intense heat

exploratory surgery - a diagnostic method to diagnose an ailment

fallopian tubes - tubes that connect the ovaries to the uterus allowing eggs to travel

gold standard - the highest standard of care

gynecologist - a physician who specializes in treating ailments of female reproductive organs

hysterectomy - a surgical operation to remove the uterus and cervix

interstitial cystitis - chronic pain that affects the bladder causing the feeling to urinate frequently, pain with sex, and is commonly found in women with endometriosis

iron deficiency anemia - when blood is lacking healthy red blood cells

irritable bowel syndrome - often abbreviated to IBS this condition causes frequent abdominal pain, diarrhea, or constipation

laparoscopic surgery - a surgery involving small incisions in the abdomen or pelvis using the aid of a camera

lo loestrin fe - a low-dose birth control pill containing two hormones (an estrogen and a progestin)

magnetic dilator - a combination of magnetic therapy inside of a dilator to lengthen soft tissue, relax muscles and pull fresh oxygenated blood to the surrounding nerves and muscles to increase healing while reducing pain

miscarriage - when an embryo or fetus dies within the first twenty weeks of pregnancy

nancy's nook endometriosis education - a Facebook group with a variety of resources along with several doctors in the group providing new research articles and information about endo

neurologist - a person specialized in the functions and disorders of nerves and the nervous system

non-continuous birth control - taking all pills in a pack including the placebo pills

norethindrone - a birth control pill that contains one hormone (progestin)

ob-gyn - an abbreviation for obstetrician and gynecology

obstetrician - a physician specialized in the care of women throughout childbirth

ovary - reproductive organ where eggs are produced

partial hysterectomy - a surgical operation to remove part of the uterus, leaving the cervix intact

pelvis - the lower part of a human between the abdomen and thighs

retrograde menstruation - when menstrual blood flows backward, up the fallopian tubes and out into the body cavity

robotic-assisted laparoscopic excision - used to diagnose and treat endometriosis by removing growths either from cutting them out or destroying them with intense heat

sonogram - a non-invasive imaging procedure that uses high-frequency sound waves to show a visual representation of internal organs, tissues, and blood flow

transvaginal ultrasound - a pelvic ultrasound where the imaging instrument is placed through the vagina to examine female reproductive organs

uterus - an organ where offspring are conceived and gestate in, as well as where the endometrium is located and sheds for menstruation

vagina - the muscular tube from the opening of the external genitals to the cervix of the uterus

vertigo - the sensation of feeling a loss of balance

Resources

Find More Information:
>The Mayo Clinic
>Hopkins Medicine
>Nancy's Nook Endometriosis Education
>VuVaTech Dilator

Find Support:
>National Sucicide Prevention Hotline (1.800.273.8255)
>RAINN (Rape, Abuse & Incest National Network)
>>(800.656.4673)

Checking the Boxes

It is important to remember that the number of symptoms and pain levels you experience does not correlate with the amount or severity of endo that you may have.

Use this page to bring to your doctor's office to make sure you mention the symptoms you are experiencing. It is easy to get overwhelmed at appointments and forget the points you wanted to discuss with your doctor.

Trust me; I've done it a dozen times.

My Symptom Checklist

☐ Painful periods

☐ Pelvic pain (with cramping that may begin before your period and extend after your menstrual cycle)

☐ Lower back and abdominal pain

☐ Pain with intercourse (during or after even to the point where you avoid it)

☐ Pain with bowel movements or urination

☐ Excessive bleeding (you may experience heavy periods, irregular periods, spotting between periods)

☐ Infertility

☐ Fatigue/lack of motivation

☐ Diarrhea

☐ Constipation

☐ Nausea (on and off of your period)

☐ Bloating (may be extreme, almost resembling a pregnant belly)

☐ Other_____

_____

_____

My Symptom Notes

Try to pack the night before your surgery, that way on the day of you only have to remember yourself.

Also, make sure you have your wallet with your identification and a charged phone! I almost forgot ID because I wasn't driving! Whoops...

If you can travel home by car on the day of the surgery, I would recommend that. The second full day after excision was the worst for me, and I couldn't imagine traveling when the pain set in.

My Surgery Checklist

☐ Pillows (you will want them for propping in bed, or sitting on for the car ride home)

☐ Bandaids (just in case there is any incision bleeding)

☐ Moist Towelettes as your bits may be sensitive

☐ Pads or panty shields as you may bleed a bit

☐ Ibprophin

☐ Snacks (endo friendly stuff easy on your tummy)

☐ Ice Pack (the hospital may give you one)

☐ Washcloths (for your head/neck/shoulders to reduce nausea or for bathing if you are unable to shower)

☐ Reusable Straws (it hurts to sit up to drink)

☐ Chapstick

☐ Clothes that have no waistbands, or high waistbands (including low rise panties and a few big tees or dresses to wear around the house and home from the hospital)

☐ Anything natural that helps nausea (peppermint, etc.)

☐ Other _____

_____

My Surgery Details

Time of Surgery:_____

Name of Hospital:_____

Location of Surgery:_____

_____

Surgery Location Phone Number:_____

Surgeon's Name:_____

Location of Surgeon/Ob-gyn's Office:_____

_____

Ob-gyn's Office Phone Number:_____

Pharmacy Name:_____

Pharmacy Location:_____

Pharmacy Phone Number:_____

Emergency Contact:_____

_____

_____

_____

Other Important Information:_____

_____

_____

_____

_____

_____

_____

_____

_____

_____

_____

_____

_____

_____

_____

_____

See and hear updates about new endometriosis news & more about Bethany's journey on her social media!

twitter.com/c/bethanystahlart
youtube.com/c/bethanystahl

About the Author

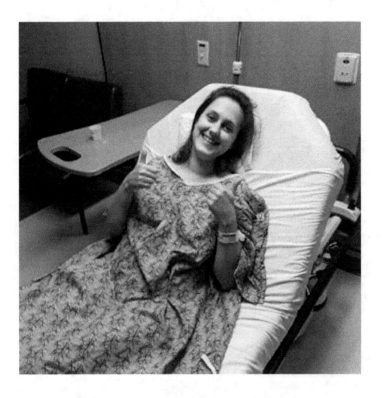

Bethany has been a strong advocate for endometriosis awareness as soon as she discovered she had been afflicted with the disease for nearly fifteen years. "Endometriosis: it's not in your head, it's in your pelvis" is Bethany's fourth published book. She aspires to continue to personify science after receiving her Bachelors in Biology.

Bethany loves spending time in nature, residing with her caring and supportive husband. She adores cuddling her fur-children who inspire her with their curiosity and innocence.

bethanystahl.com

Stay Strong,
Warrior!

Love,
Bethany

Printed in the USA
CPSIA information can be obtained
at www.ICGtesting.com
LVHW011917040624
782270LV00004B/475